KU-160-013

PTERANODON

CORYTHOSAURUS

PROTOCERATOPS

VELOCIRAPTOR

ALLOSAURUS

CRYOLOPHOSAURUS

TRACHODON

TYRANNOSAURUS REX

SUPERSAURUS

PARASAUROLOPHUS

First published by the Blue Sky Press, an Imprint of Scholastic Inc., USA, as
How Do Dinosaurs Learn Their Colors? in 2006 and *How Do Dinosaurs Count to Ten?* in 2004
New edition published in paperback in Great Britian by Harper Collins Children's Books in 2007
This edition published 2010

ISBN 978-0-00-786515-4

1 3 5 7 9 10 8 6 4 2

HarperCollins Children's Books is a division of HarperCollins Publishers Ltd.
Text copyright © Jane Yolen 2004, 2006
Illustrations copyright © Mark Teague 2004, 2006
All rights reserved. Published by arrangement with Scholastic Inc. 557 Broadway, New York, NY 10012, U
The author and illustrator assert the moral right to be identified as the author and illustrator of the work
A CIP catalogue record for this title is available from the British Library. All rights reserved.
No part of this publication may be reproduced, stored in a retrieval system or transmitted in any
form or by any means, electronic, mechanical, photocopying, recording or otherwise, without the prior
permission of HarperCollins Publishers Ltd, 77-85 Fulham Palace Road, Hammersmith, London W6 8JF
Visit our website at: www.harpercollinschildrensbooks.co.uk
Printed in China

JANE YOLEN

How Do Dinosaurs Learn Colours and Numbers?

Illustrated by

MARK TEAGUE

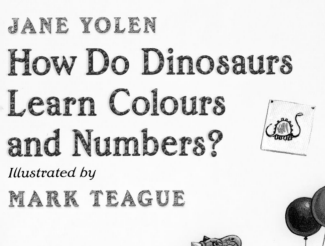

HarperCollins *Children's Books*

How Do Dinosaurs
Learn Colours?

Dinosaur colours

start with red:

GORGOSAURUS

A **red** fire engine

tucked under the bed,

a **purple** towel

left on the floor,

GALLIMIMUS

a **green** sign taped

to the bedroom door,

a **blue** robe thrown

across two chairs,

a **pink** ball
bouncing down
the stairs,

ANKYLOSAURUS

yellow bananas
right by a plate,

brown circles

all around a date,

white chalk marks

on an old **black** slate

VELOCIRAPTOR

and an orange backpack –

don't be late!

Rainbows here

and rainbows there...

CRYOLOPHOSAURUS

Dinosaur colours

everywhere!

How Do Dinosaurs
Learn Numbers?

Dinosaur counting
starts with one.
One tattered
teddy bear
just for fun.

TYRANNOSAURUS REX

Two big balloons

tied to the bed,

three toy trucks painted

blue, green and red.

Four balls that bounce,

CORYTHOSAURUS

five big letter blocks

and under the bed,

six dirty socks.

A track, an engine

and seven cars,

STEGOSAURUS

an easel with eight

full paint jars.

Nine pictures hanging

on the wall,

ten books to read –
and that is all.

Now that he's counted
from one to ten,
how does
a dinosaur
count again?

APATOSAURUS

AGAIN!